Frostic

Rustleaf

Porte Sumac

Wolfepointe

Lonepine

Grasslake

...harbor

Burl

Sandmason

Venn

Lillygrove

Oakgrove

Birchflow

Flintrust

Willowroot

Wild Country

N

1108
TERRITORIES
of the MICE

* village * town * city

In these we claim our
independence from the
savage world around.
Our autonomy, ideals, &
pride live here. By our
mettle it survives.

FOR MY WIFE JULIA

SPECIAL THANKS TO:
MY PARENTS, JESSE GLENN, MIKE DAVIS, EMERSON JONES,
SEYTH MIERSMA, JEREMY BASTIAN, NATE PRIDE, KATIE COOK,
ALEX SHEIKMAN, SEAN RUBIN, DUNCAN FEGREDO,
C.P. WILSON III, SHANE-MICHAEL VIDAURRI, MIKE MIGNOLA,
MARK SMYLIE, ERIC LYNCH,
AND TERRY JONES

MOUSE GUARD™
THE BLACK AXE

STORY & ART BY
DAVID PETERSEN

MOUSE GUARD: Volume Three: THE BLACK AXE

ISBN: 9780857681430

Published by Titan Books,
a division of Titan Publishing Group Ltd.
144 Southwark Street, London SE1 0UP

A CIP catalogue record for this book
is available from the British Library.

Printed in China

This edition first published July 2013
10 9 8 7 6 5 4 3 2 1

Did you enjoy this book? We love to hear from our readers. Please e-mail us at: readerfeedback@titanemail.com or write to Reader Feedback at the above address.

To receive advance information, news, competitions, and exclusive offers online, please sign up for the Titan newsletter on our website:
www.titanbooks.com

www.titanbooks.com

PREFACE

WELCOME TO THE WORLD OF CELANAWE.

MOUSE GUARD: THE BLACK AXE LURES US INTO BELIEVING MICE FLY BIRDS, BUILD SHIPS, AND KILL FOXES. THAT FERRETS LIVE IN GREAT HALLS, THAT WEASELS WEAR SKULLS, AND THAT MICE CAROUSE WITH THE BEST OF THEM.

THE DETAIL OF THE MEDIEVAL PERIOD IS AUTHENTIC AND FEELS JUST AS IT SHOULD. THE COSTUMES, THE BOOKS, THE INNS, THE HOUSES, THE LIBRARIES, ALL LOOK AS IF THEY WERE MADE IN THE MIDDLE AGES.

I CANNOT PRAISE DAVID PETERSEN TOO HIGHLY FOR HIS STORYTELLING. HE KNOWS EXACTLY WHEN TO SAY WHAT IS HAPPENING IN THE TEXT AND DIALOGUE, AND EXACTLY WHEN TO LEAVE IT TO THE PICTURES TO TELL THE STORY.

MOREOVER, YOU ACTUALLY CARE FOR THE CREATURES IN THE TALE. FOR EXAMPLE, THE FERRETS WHEN YOU FIRST SEE THEM ARE COARSE AND DANGEROUS, BUT YOU DISCOVER THEY HAVE A CODE OF HONOR THAT ELEVATES THEM, AND WHEN THE KING'S SON IS BROUGHT IN DEAD, YOU FEEL FOR THE KING'S GRIEF. THE IMAGES OF THE FERRETS AT EM'S FUNERAL ARE SIMPLY STUNNING.

CELANAWE HIMSELF IS A GREAT HERO – QUIET BUT RESOURCEFUL AND DETERMINED – WHILE STILL BEING A MOUSE.

THE TALE OF *THE BLACK AXE* IS TRUE TO THE SPIRIT OF THE MEDIEVAL PERIOD AND A WONDERFUL READ. I HOPE YOU ENJOY IT AS MUCH AS I DID.

TERRY JONES
LONDON MARCH 2013

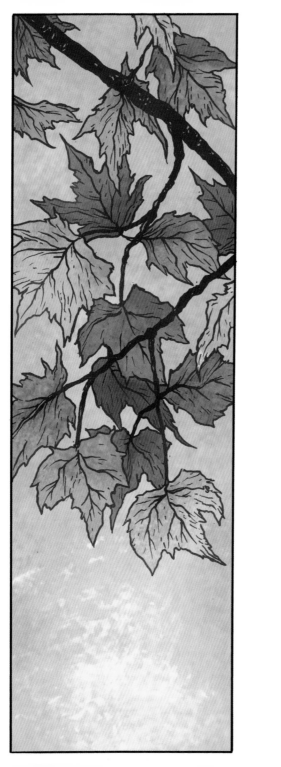

CONTENTS

PROLOGUE

CHAPTER ONE
CHAPTER TWO
CHAPTER THREE
CHAPTER FOUR
CHAPTER FIVE
CHAPTER SIX

EPILOGUE

MAPS, GUIDES, AND ASSORTED EXTRAS

PINUP GALLERY

ABOUT THE AUTHOR

PROLOGUE

Spring 1153: six days before day and night are equal.

As predicted, the last eight days have been filled with rain.

The rivers and streams are now rushing above their banks.

I have sent out nearly every Guard I have into this most demanding season.

Spring brings with it the need to rebuild and repair what was destroyed over winter or during the thaw.

Every town requires our attention, every path between needs to be scouted again.

And the weather, while warmer, seems more angry than any winter storm could offer.

Predators are waking and breeding.

My mice are working mainly in pairs to cover all the ground our work takes us through.

Three full moon cycles have come and gone since our youngest Guard, Lieam, vanished.

I can spare none to search for him though.

Whitepine
wood

Mice who knew Lieam from patrol...

...will inquire with the towns to see if they have seen our redfur.

But I instructed them that their focus needs to be on the needs of the territories above one lost mouse.

Lockhaven

Tindale

Later matriarchs might think me cold-hearted for not spending more resources on a Guard whose acts have made such notable entries in this journal for the last thirteen seasons.

I am inclined to believe Saxon knows more than he is letting on about Lieam, but I see the worry in his and Kenzie's faces as well.

I assure any who read this that I wish for nothing but the safe return of that mouse.

Our first seasonal summit is to occur at Lockhaven in ten days time.

The leaders from across the territories are being escorted by each of the settlements' sons and daughters that wish to become Guardmice.

A trial by fire, or rain as will be the case, will test their desire to start a life purely of service.

I admit the loss of Celanawe, has rattled my sense of security.

I did not know the myth was truly protecting us, and when I found that he was, we lost him forever.

Mice have risen above the ability to survive in this world to a level of prosperity we have grown accustom to.

I fear without the Black Axe, we will need to go back to a more primitive way of life.

Are the territories too large to govern themselves?

If so, they are certainly too large to be governed by one.

Dorigift Gilfsledge

These terrors are nothing new for a Matriarch...

...not even to one so young as I, who had an open declaration of war against another species.

This foe is more troubling though...

...It has no one name, no face, no home.

It looms like a dark giant...

half asleep...

half awake.

My only hope is that the Guard together with the common mice...

...can placate it until we have a new hero in which to believe.

—Gwendolyn
Spring 1153

THE BLACK AXE

In secret, the **Black Axe** worked his will toward the land, and lo, the beasts of fur who stand on four and growl with great rumbling throats, lived in fear. The feathered and the scaled too shivered at the unknown mouse with his beaked blade. His weapon was mighty and his duty was just.

Spring 1115:
One Moon cycle before
Summer begins.

I had worked in the
spring chill for nearly a
season on the construction
of a new Frostic outpost.

The old one was little more
than a hole in the ground.

I was tired that day.

I did not know it was the day
my life would change forever.

I also did not know that the same season an aged mouse in Appleloft named Em discovered she was the next to last of her family line.

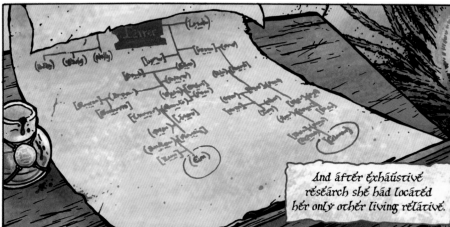

And after exhaustive research she had located her only other living relative.

Em had lived alone for over forty seasons.

She preferred company of a feathered nature, and had a kinship with them.

At Frostic, I in many ways also enjoyed solitude.

The tenderpaws I trained that season were forced to locate me...

or 'lesson one,' as I told them.

I feel Guardmice do best out of doors anyhow, in open country.

It keeps our eyes opened, our fur moving, and our ears closer to the beasts and soil...

...always listening.

Yet this day I was returning to Lockhaven, citadel of the Mouse Guard.

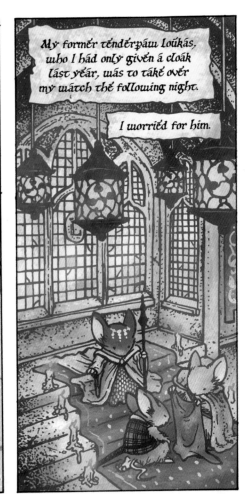

My former tenderpaw Loukas, who I had only given a cloak last year, was to take over my watch the following night.

I worried for him.

Though he was a capable mouse, I smelled that larger mating beasts were roaming the shoreline near Frostic, something seasoned veterans of the Guard avoid facing at all costs.

When ready to begin my three day journey, I heard something overhead.

At first, I thought it to be a predator...

...She was no threat to me though.

I did not even fear her scavenging mount.

Though not a Guardmouse, I gathered she could have been, in her day.

It was then that my fur stood on end. Larger beasts were near.

Their odor arrived before they did.

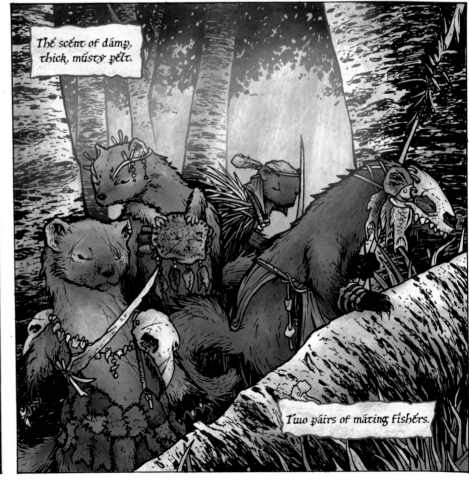

The scent of damp, thick, musty pelt.

Two pairs of mating fishers.

HE PRONOUNCES IT "KHEL-EN-AWE."

Not yet knowing her loyalties, I fibbed.

QUICKLY! AWAY FROM HERE.

AND I CAN TAKE YOU TO HIM.

The shoreline was too exposed. I wanted the cover of leaf and grass.

FOLLOW.

WAIT! I HAVE TRAVELED A LONG WAY TO COME SEE....

...YOU.

Something I learned training tenderpaws: lead and they will follow.

TAKE ME NO FURTHER...

...FOR **YOU** ARE CELANAWE.

SON OF MAREIN, DAUGHTER OF BLACKBUR, SON OF HOLTON, SON OF DALTON.

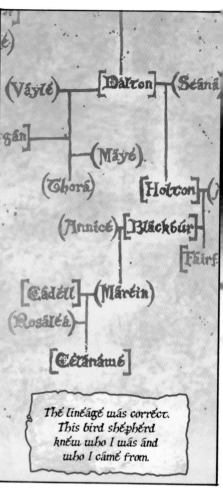

(Vayle) [Dalton] (Seana)

gan

(Maye)

(Thora) [Holton]

(Annice) [Blackbur]

[Fairf

[Cadell] (Marein)

(Rosalea)

[Celanawe]

The lineage was correct. This bird shepherd knew who I was and who I came from.

WE ARE KIN YOU AND I.

FROM LOCK-HAVEN I HAVE FLOWN...

...AND FROM APPLELOFT BEFORE THAT.

I HAVE THE AUTHORITY OF—

WE MUST LEAVE THIS PLACE MAKING NO SOUND.

FOR WE ARE HUNTED...

CAW CAW

Her horror awoke in her an understanding of the danger.

Quietly, we left the shore into the wood and quietly we hid.

ARE YOU NOT A GUARD?

I'D FIGHT ONE OF ANYTHING BEFORE TAKING ON A PACK OF SOME BEAST.

Their senses were too good for us to have gone unnoticed, though.

Quickly we were pursued.

Avoidance was our only effective weapon.

When its hot breath was gone, I knew it was as well.

Sneaking by, we saw the reason.

One of them had caught a squirrel...

...and two others wanted to share in the spoils.

Clearly, hunger was not their only motivation...

These hunters wore their determination for prey as adornment.

I had already lost track of one of the deadly foursome.

By land we were destined to be caught.

Fishers, despite their name, care naught for being in deep water...

...so it was by sea that I saw our escape.

But my plan was already failing...

Boat material was less than ideal there.

It was then that I heard the missing one, high above...

...sure that it was imagining my taste and how I would feel in its gullet.

QUACK QUACK

QUACK QUACK

QUACK QUACK QUACK

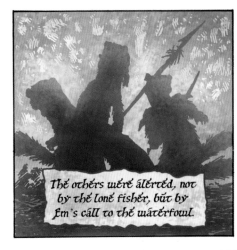

The others were alerted, not by the lone fisher, but by Em's call to the waterfowl.

YOU...

CHAPTER TWO

On the backs of winged beasts and furred giants, strode the Black Axe

They took no notice of him, for his movements were quiet and his soul calm.

The land was wide and vast and he could round all that was from rising till setting of the moon.

Port Sumac is really two towns. Atop the cliffs, where residents live, is the town proper.

Their namesake's growth offers a supply of dried leaf for pipe and tankards of Rhus Ale while there.

Come Winter, the upper dwellings are full. However from the dawn of Spring until the extinguishing of Fall...

...below is where most mice think when they hear the town's name.

The rock face plummets into the deep and shoreless sea.

Docks, moored ships, and floating dwellings lashed together form the heart of the Port.

Goods for coin and coin for goods. Everything was for sale.

The practical: food, gear, seeds, cloth, clay vessels...

The impractical: pendants to ward off the dead, elixirs promising long life, and bone chips which tell the future...

And the impossible. According to Em we were in the market for a ship and a boat mouse willing to sail us off the edge of any map.

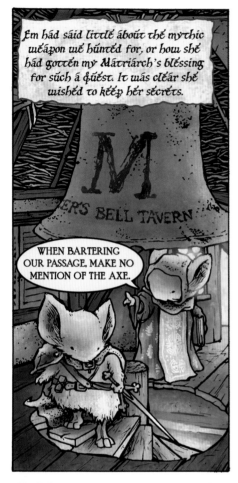

Em had said little about the mythic weapon we hunted for, or how she had gotten my Matriarch's blessing for such a quest. It was clear she wished to keep her secrets.

ER'S BELL TAVERN

WHEN BARTERING OUR PASSAGE, MAKE NO MENTION OF THE AXE.

HOW DO YOU EXPECT ME TO DO THAT?

A CLEVER GUARD YOU ARE, I AM SURE YOU WILL MANAGE...

UNLESS YOU NEED AN AGED LADY MOUSE TO DEAL WITH THESE SCOUNDRELS.

The Mariner's Bell catered to the filthiest, crookedest, and greediest mice in the territories. Everything had a price: ruling power, murder, even mice themselves.

however, buying a mouse's service is no easy feat with less coin than three tankards worth of ale.

YA UNGRATEFUL FLEA BAG!

YER DAD WERE A CAPTAIN. YA CAN LAY NO CLAIM TO HIS DEEDS FER YERSELF.

MY FATHER LEFT ME THAT SHIP AND ALL THE TITLE THAT GOES WITH IT...

LUCKY, YE ARE. THAT AYE'S LETTIN YA KEEP HIS SHIP...

YA RUM SOAKED PELT OF MUMBLES AND GIBBERISH.

YER CHEATIN' ME OUTTA WHAT'S MINE, ROARKE!

The younger mouse wasn't as grizzled, rough, and dead in the eyes as the others. But his fur was stiff from the sea salt and I could catch a whiff of spirits from his muzzle.

The morning next, Conrad and I loaded his ship with goods needed for our journey, bought with coin provided by Em.

She however sat silently scrawling in her book.

CAPTAIN'S CAPTAIN EH?

T'WERE MY FATHER'S ROLE AND RIGHTFULLY MINE THEN.

I SUSPECT ROARKE MURDERED HIM FOR IT WHILE I...ER...

HAD A JUG TOO MANY.

NO.

ACROSS THE NORTHERN SEA UNTIL WE HIT A NEW SHORE.

I HONOR MY BARGAINS, EVEN WITH FILTH LIKE ROARKE, AND YOU SHOULD, TOO.

WE COULD JUST SAIL DOWN TO LILLYGROVE NEAR THE ISLE OF VENN—

I questioned my own judgement that day. I was blindly following Em off the edge of the world for a mythological axe that no mouse had seen in twenty seasons.

Was I no better than Conrad? Manipulated into this quest?

Only because I knew my matriarch Bronwyn's writing, her script, her seal, would I honor Em's request.

At my insistence that I get word back to Bronwyn before departure, Em secured my sealed return message to a willing insect that she charmed.

She assured me it understood when she told it "Lockhaven."

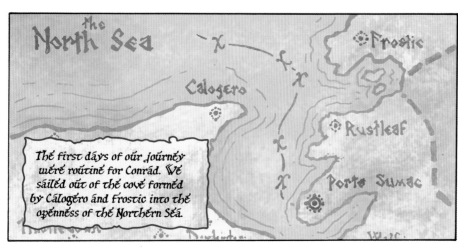

the
North Sea

x

✧ Frostic

Calogero

✧ Rustleaf

✧ Porte Sumac

The first days of our journey were routine for Conrad. We sailed out of the cove formed by Calogero and Frostic into the openness of the Northern Sea.

Early on, I tried to plot our course by map. Once we lost sight of land, this became impossible.

Conrad said he had little use for maps anyhow.

Em, however, would make note of stars once they appeared, finding constellations to guide us.

The Clay Pot.

The harvester's Scythe.

The heron.

The weather taunted our progress. Days of the new summer's sun baked us...

...then the skies opened at night for a downpour in the dark.

On the seventeenth day we lost sight of all birds.

I rationed our supplies even tighter then, knowing before hitting land, we had at least just as far to go as we had come.

Several times I tried to interrogate 'em about our quest and the Black Axe, but she always moved her eyes to our newest companion the boat mouse and grew quiet.

Finally, on the night of our thirty-second day at sea, Em and I had our chance to speak.

Conrad was sleeping very soundly with the help of his last jug of spirits.

So, Em began recalling the Axe's creation.

Every young mouse knows the legend of Farrer...

FARRER:

...who forged a great Black Axe due to his sorrow.

He took it to Lockhaven so one mouse could avenge the death of Farrer's family.

LOCKHAVEN...

Em claimed this tale was no legend.

She explained that unknown to most, Farrer later remarried and started his family anew.

MOST BELIEVED FARRER TO HAVE DIED ALONE AFTER FORGING THE AXE.

BUT HIS BLOODLINE CONTINUED IN SECRET...

YOU AND I ARE THE LAST LIVING DESCENDANTS OF THAT LINE.

Using all manner of beast: furred...

...feathered...

...and insect, Em searched for the Axe without leaving Appleloft.

Her beastly informants revealed Em's elder brother Benn to be the last mouse to lay paw on the weapon.

And that he was last seen on a shore across "Storvänd Sea"...

...which she explained is what we call The Northern Sea.

If we were the last of the living Färrer kin, Em expected her brother had perished there...

Em, Benn, and I...

All of our mutual blood...tied to the mythic Axe of old...

WHAT ARE YOU TWO WHISPERING ABOUT OVER THAT BOOK?

ONLY REVIEWING EM'S SKETCHES OF THE CONSTELLATIONS.

After that night, Conrad's jug was empty and he remained alert, only sleeping briefly every few days.

I didn't know why he wanted to stay awake...until we had a few close calls with unknown monsters from the deep.

KILL SOMETHING THAT LARGE AND IT WILL EITHER MAKE THE WORLD CRUMBLE OR MAKE YOU MORE LEGEND THAN MOUSE.

The tenderpaws I encountered had a need to serve...a selfless drive for their fellow mouse. Conrad, it seemed, was just an opportunist...

...waiting for one great event that would land him a title in that den of trade for him to ride out the rest of his days upon.

Fortunately, no sea beast gave him long enough of a chance.

Even with my extended rationing, our larders were spent.

The toll of our fifty-six days at sea had cleaned out the supplies in the ship's hull.

Had it not been for collected rainwater from recent storms, I'm sure we would have perished.

Conrad caught a few small fish and even one large one...

...that must have towed the ship a day's journey behind course.

Conrad convinced Em and me to partake in the spoils.

I had never eaten the flesh of a beast before.

BLEARRH

It would take near starvation before I would do it again.

If my stomach hadn't been sour enough that night, the most severe storm of my life would make it worse.

The sound of the crashing sea, rumbling thunder, and cracking lightning was only matched by the creaking and moaning of the timbers we had called home for nearly two moon cycles.

Seeing the impending swell, we lashed any loose item of value to ourselves.

When it crashed onto us, the ship was torn asunder and swallowed by the inky wetness.

I lost sight of 'em in the dark waves.

The second wave that hit pushed everything away...

Then I, too, choked on the salty sea, and my vision went to black.

CHAPTER THREE

The blade of the axe was honed, but not
as sharp as the tongue and mind of
its wielder. For he had the
cunning of Reinhard,
first of the
Vulpes

Rare was
the time when
blood did not need
to be spilled for prosperity
to spread for mice, but when it did
not it was due to the Black Axe's words
entering like a poison into the veins of his prey

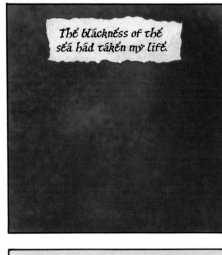

The blackness of the sea had taken my life.

When breath came...I thought it must have been ethereal vapor entering my body as I journeyed to Séyán.

As my eyes opened, I saw what bore resemblance to where legends say the souls of virtuous mice dwell.

Then pain awoke in my body and I knew this was no afterlife.

I had bones that were surely broken and my mind ached with all the ferocity of the storm that brought me here...

...us here...

In neither direction along the shore did we find Conrad. I silently mourned him as we searched.

Was this even the land we had set out for?

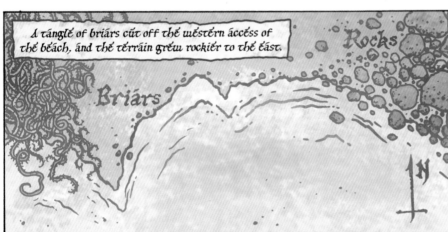

A tangle of briars cut off the western access of the beach, and the terrain grew rockier to the east.

Rocks

Briars

N

The skeleton and clothes of one of our own, tucked in the stones, told us it was.

Em and I worked our way north where the crows indicated the hall in the hill was.

At a distance, it had looked quite small, but arriving at the gates we thought it surely to be occupied by beasts much larger than ourselves.

WE HAVE LITTLE CHANCE OF OPENING THOSE GATES...

MY BROTHER'S MURDERER AND THE BLADE OF FARRER LIE INSIDE THAT HALL!

HAVE YOU NO CARE FOR THE SPILLED BLOOD OF OUR MUTUAL KIN AND ITS LEGACY?

My passion for the quest felt less of an obligation to past relatives than to the duty I had to the command of my Matriarch.

But even a cousin as distant as Em did feel like kin after such a time together.

I ONLY REFUSE TO OPEN THEM.

ARE WE NOT MICE?

CAN WE NOT GO UNDER THEM?

DO YOU SMELL THAT...?

FIRE?

NO, FERRETS...

THE CROWS...

THEY GAVE US WORD THAT A MOUSE CAME TO THESE GATES FIVE YEARS AGO...

HA! THOSE BIRDS HAVE GOOD MEMORIES.

BACK THEN, MY HUNTERS HEARD WHISPERS FROM THE BEASTS ON THE ISLE...

A CREATURE HAS COME TO TAKE THIS LAND AS HIS OWN.

HIS SPECIES WILL RULE.

AND HE WILL MAKE ROOM FOR HIS KIN ATOP THE BONES OF HIS ENEMIES.

HOWEVER, NO CREATURE HAD SEEN THE INVADER OR COULD POINT TO THE SOURCE OF THE RUMOR.

THEN, AT THE FEAST ON THE LONGEST DAY OF THE YEAR THERE CAME A THUDDING ON THE GATES OF MY HALL.

THUD
THUD
THUD

THE ONE WHO INTENDED TO MURDER MY KIND WAS ONLY A MOUSE.

MY SUBJECTS LAUGH BECAUSE WITH EASE I CLEAVED THE UPSTART IN TWO AND SWALLOWED BOTH PARTS WHOLE...

CLOTHES, BONES, AND ALL.

W-WAIT... YOU SAY THERE WERE NO REMAINS?

DID THIS MOUSE HAVE TITLE?

"MEREK." AND THIS IS THE WEAPON HE RAISED AGAINST ME.

Our quest.

Proof the tale of Farrer was more than a story scribbled on paper, knit in cloth, and whispered into our ears.

THOUGH UNFAIRLY RAISED AGAINST YOU,

I CELANAWE, A MOUSE OF THE NOBLE GUARD OF LOCKHAVEN, FROM SHORES DISTANT FROM YOUR OWN, REQUEST RETURN OF THE AXE...

AS IT IS THE PROPERTY OF MOUSE AND NOT OF FERRET.

NAY.

IT HAS HUNG FROM MY BELT FOR OVER TWENTY SEASONS.

IT'S A SYMBOL OF WHAT HAPPENS TO THOSE WHO SQUANDER MY GOOD WILL AND FAIR RULE.

I WEAR IT AS A REMINDER TO ALL

OF WHAT CAN COME TO CREATURES, WITHOUT CLAIM, THREATENING WHAT IS MINE.

I BEG YOUR PARDON, FAIR KING, BUT WOULD IT NOT BE MY OWN FUNERAL THEN?

I AM SO WILLING...

SEEMS I HAVE NOTHING MORE TO LOSE...

THE AXE.

CELANAWE WILL NEED THE AXE FOR THE TASK.

THE DEAL IS STRUCK, ELDER MOUSE.

CELANAWE, RETURN WITH PROOF OF THE DEFEAT OF MINE ENEMY, AND YOU BOTH SHALL WALK FREELY FROM MY GATES WITH THIS WEAPON IN YOUR PAW.

BUT IF TWO SUNDOWNS PASS WITH NO PROOF, YOUR EM WILL BE THE FIRST BITE OF MY NEXT FEAST...

AND MY KIN WILL HUNT YOU DOWN AS THE LAST BITE OF IT.

And into the dark I marched.

The beaked axe wrought by my forebear was heavier than my sword. Upon it I carried the weight of the fates of not only £m and myself, but also a cunning fox.

After that storm I had thought I'd awoken on the shores of a glorious afterlife...

...and now I walked into the thorny bowels of the horror it must be like to die, only to find there is no afterlife at all.

CHAPTER FOUR

AT THE SHORE OF
THE GREAT LARGE LAKE,
THE BATTLE-FOR-ALL
BEGAN

Lupis showed snarled tooth and wicked claw

Buteo soared above with eyes that could see all

Vulpes sculled about with tactics above all others

Serpentes rode low with venom for a blade

THE BLACK AXE TOOK SEVEN SUNS WORTH OF TIME ON EACH
OF THEM AND THEIR KIN THAT FOLLOWED THEM TO BATTLE
AND WHEN THE MOON HAD SHOWED EVERY PHASE
THE GREAT LAKE SHONE SCARLET WITH THE LIFE
OF THE BLACK AXE'S VICTIMS

As a Guardmouse we rarely openly hunt larger predators.

When we do, we are in great numbers and doing so because the beast leaves us no choice.

A lone mouse, even with the mythic Black Axe, was at poor odds against a single fox in its own lair.

Yet my kin's life and my oath to the Guard's Matriarch Bronwyn left me no other option than to slay the creature.

If there were a moon or stars visible that night, they did not reach through the layers of bramble above my head.

None of Em's navigating tricks would have worked.

My stomach ached with hunger...how many days had it been since I'd eaten?

With every turn I made, I became less sure of my path and my surroundings.

Was the great orange beast watching me?

Were my tiny cuts from the thorns offering a path of the scent of my blood for it to follow?

What was a horrible mess of untamed growth now looked like an unnatural landscape of obscurity.

Early that next morning, the cool chill of the night mixed with the dampness of the thicketed shore and the rising sun.

With my sword I would have attempted to pierce it, but I may have only told myself that at the time.

My fear seized over me, making me as silent as my foe...

And it slipped past me and into the fog again.

...And lost them again.

That was when the fox found us instead.

I felt Conrád's zéal against thé fox hád léss to do with mÿ or Ém's wéll-béing and moré to do with his lúst for thé séat of Cáptáin's Cáptáin sáving thé Black Axé would éarn him.

I saw their short stalemate as a chance to strike a mortal blow...

...and to save Conrad's life.

ARRRrRRrrrrrr!

With á tug from Conrad's hook, thé fox shifted ánd thé áncient bládé missèd its márk.

I pushed through the tighter brambles and led the fox inward.

The mad beast became tangled in its own maze...

The walls of its home turned into a thorny net.

Later I went about the dirty work of collecting proof of the beast's demise...

...when we heard more sounds of breaking twigs and branches.

My mind wandered back to what I had told 'em: "I'd fight one of anything before taking on a pack of some beast."

They sat together, as though inseparable.

They were nought but kits.

Conrad and I had just slain their mother.

And not for Mouse-kind, but for Ferret, and for the bounty of this axe.

I HAVE NO LUST FOR THEIR BLOOD.

I SLAYED WHAT THE KING OF THIS ISLE SAW AS A THREAT. THESE TWO POSE NO HARM TO HIM OR HIS KIN FOR MANY SEASONS YET.

THEY ARE NOT PART OF THE BARGAIN.

THEY WILL BE EASIER TO BRING DOWN THAN THE LARGE ONE...

for the first time in my life, I felt pity for a predator.

These kits had done nothing and hadn't even asked to be born.

They were old enough to stay alive so long as Lúthébon's subjects didn't hunt them.

STAY IN THESE THORNS.

In my lowest grumble I tried to imitate their bark as fm had caused words to the crows.

GROW TALL, BEFORE YOU LEAVE THIS PLACE.

HUNTERS WAIT FOR YOU OUTSIDE.

If they understood, they showed no sign but to stay together, rooted to the spot we found them.

The sun was starting its descent toward the horizon when we arrived at the hill where Ildur Hall stood, and we entered the doors as the sky blushed orange.

KING LUTHEBON, AN ORB OF YOUR ENEMY'S GAZE LAYS IN THIS SACK AS PROOF I HELD MY END OF THE BARGAIN.

Luthebon wore an odd expression on his muzzle.

I assumed it to be Conrad's sudden appearance on his mouse-less island.

AND THIS GREYFUR WAS THE THIRD IN OUR PARTY WE THOUGHT TO BE LOST TO SEA.

WE ARE COMPLETE ONCE AGAIN—

It was then I saw the reason for the king's troubled look.

Em's body was empty of life.

Death had taken her.

CHAPTER FIVE

After he had lost all loves, and seen the fruits of his work benefit all those around,

The Black Axe thought the weapon to be a burden and wished to end his nameless existence. He sought out the bloodline of

FARRER

one of his children's children may have the will and strength to carry the burden. As he found each descendant, he saw their lives to be full and with promise of new trades, young, and love.

he and the axe were forever to be one

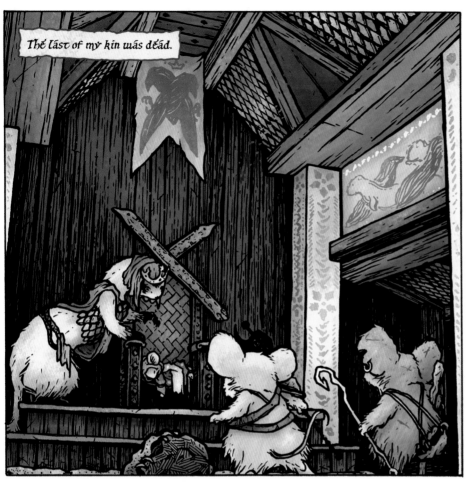

The last of my kin was dead.

TREACHEROUS FERRET! YOUR BLOOD WILL STAIN THESE FLOORS AND YOUR—

I DID NOT KILL HER, BRAVE MOUSE...

His controlled voice hung in the air with regret and shame.

MY SUBJECT, EBEROCHRE, TOOK NO HEED OF MY COMMAND NOT TO TOUCH YOUR EM.

HE, MY HEALER, GREEDILY SOUGHT TO UNDERSTAND HER MORE, FOR HE HAD NEVER SEEN A LIVE MOUSE TO STUDY.

COVETING EM AS A SPECIMEN, HE SNATCHED HER UP, AND IN SO DOING, WOUNDED HER TINY FRAME.

WITH MALICE ENOUGH FOR THE BOTH OF US, CELANAWE, I RAN THE FOOL THROUGH.

MY WORD AND MY HONOR ARE WORTH MORE TO ME THAN THE LIFE OF ONE OF MY OWN...

...CERTAINLY MORE THAN ONE WHOM DOES NOT UNDERSTAND VIRTUE.

KILLIN' MICE IS WHAT YOU FILTHY WEASEL-KIN LOVE TO DO, AS SURE AS YER HEART BEATS.

JUST AS WE MICE CAN'T HELP BUT WANT TO SLAY EVERY LAST ONE OF YOU FOR IT.

I HAVE NO DESIRE TO KILL WITHOUT NEEDING THE MEAT.

HOARDING, KILLING FOR SPORT, AND THE FILLING OF LARDERS IS THE WORK OF OTHER SPECIES OF WEASEL

WE TRIED TO MEND HER WOUND.

BUT THE DAMAGE WAS DONE, AND WITHIN MOMENTS, SHE WAS GONE

My heart sank heavily while my blood boiled. The Axe's history continued its tradition of being steeped in the loss of loved ones as surely as it had with its forger.

When I was able to climb back to land, I swung the Axe a few times, letting the feel of its heavy impact comfort me.

A few well-landed blows could bring down the fox.

I let a calm wash over me, waiting to strike the shape when it emerged from the fog...

CONRAD?!?

At án inlánd stréám knouun ás Bellisflod, uué láid þm to rest.

YE WERE A TOUGH OLD GIRL, EM. HAD IT NOT BEEN FOR WEASEL CLAW, YE WOULDA OUTLIVED US ALL, I SPECT.

Conrad and I kept clear of the ferrets in the following days.

I sat reading Em's journal on the Axe. I hoped its history, words, and pictures would give me an understanding of how recovering this ebony blade was worth the loss of her life.

Eyes dazed and mind numb from her passing, I took in very little meaning from the old text and notes...

...until midsun on the sixth day after her death, my eyes hit one of the last passages clearly in Em's writing:

RETURN WITH THE AXE TO SHORESTONE, Speak to haven guild, keepers of the ideals of LOCKE, OMARR, FARRER, and THURSTON

MMM... CONRAD....

EH?

LUTHEBON PROMISED US FREE LIVES HERE...

...BUT I BELIEVE WE SHOULD RETURN TO THE TERRITORIES OF MICE.

The prospect of finding more meaning in this axe and Em's quest still being incomplete were only parts of my desire to return. Conrad and I were alone in our species there.

NOTHIN' WOULD MAKE ME HAPPIER THAN LEAVIN'...

...'CEPT RETAKING CAPTAIN'S CAPTAIN FROM THAT FLEA-PELT ROARKE.

THOUGH, I'VE ONE LESS LEG THAN I STARTED WITH AN' WALKIN' 'CROSS THE SEA ON ONLY ONE LEG IS QUITE A TRICK.

We had both left lives behind us on that other land. As Conrad said, his desire to reclaim his father's seat in Port Sumac drew him home.

And I was still a Guard.

The leader of my order, Bronwyn, was at Lockhaven.

She was my secret love, and I hers. Between a future of no love on Ildur or risking death to return to her...

...I chose love.

Between twenty dawns and dusks, Lúthebon's subjects and I built a new ship.

As none of us were trained in the craft, it was not as great a ship as Conrad's old one...

...but it floated and had rigging and a tiller even I could understand.

Lúthébon hád somé séá ánd stár chárts, uhich, coúpléd uith ém's notés, gávé ús á béáring.

Ildur

Soíl and Frozenroutes of the
Lands of the Ebon Kingdom
Crown of Luth

VOYAGE OF THE
RED SNAPPER

Though ué figúréd it woúld táké ús longér to rétúrn this wáy, ué álso folloued bird migrátions.

Théy léd ús to othér smáll islánds whéré ué coúld réplénish oúr stock of bérriés, sééds, ánd léávés.

Time started to remove the sting of Em's passing, and the voyage with Conrad were some of the best days of my life.

We chatted about memories of our fathers...

TAUGHT ME TA SAIL, HE DID. AND TO BARTER WITH THE BEST OF 'EM WHEN I WAS ONLY A SEASON OVER FIVE.

FATHER CARED FOR ME, I SUPPOSE, BUT SHOWED HIS TENDERNESS TOWARD MY SISTER ROSALEA.

WHEN SHE DIED YOUNG FROM ILLNESS, HE STOWED THAT WARMTH DEEP INSIDE HIM AND NEVER SHARED IT AGAIN.

Conrád wás ás roúgh ánd coárse ás hé hád béen thé dáy I mét him. Thoúgh I think hé wás thé bétter for this tráit.

Othér micé woúld'vé lost spirit áftér thé lég incidént. Conrád took to thé loss álmost ás thoúgh hé hád béen born withoút thát párticúlár páw.

Port Súmác héld powér ovér him, thoúgh. Whéré hé wás willing to overcomé ány obstáclé ánd fight whén it cámé to his lég, hé poúted ánd fússéd ovér whát hé wás "owéd" in thát city.

Hé úséd words I won't répéat aboút thé micé théré.

Whén I súggéstéd hé stárt ovér élséwhéré, án ángry glint shoné in his éyés whilé hé'd sáy shárply:

NAH. 'TIS MINE.

AN' I'LL BE COMIN' FOR IT.

Conrád hád númérous quéstions ábout thé Gúárd ánd its opérátions ánd symbolism...

THE CLOAK'S COLOR HAS MEANIN' TO THE MOUSE, AYE?

YES. MY MENTOR, GENEVRA, HAD IT DYED COAL GREY, A SYMBOL OF "MATURE DETERMINATION."

IN OVER SIXTY SEASONS IT FADED TO THAT COLOR.

Hé áskéd othér quéstions, ábout my ágé, thé áxé, hou I hád comé to losé it, ánd hou Lúthébon cámé to oun it. I dodgéd mány of thésé quéstions ánd péppéréd my ávoidáncé uith ánsuérs thát cámé from vágué légénd.

We took better care to map our way...

...found small unplotted islands...

...camped two moon phases in the snow and ice...

...and even crafted songs about the trip.

Away for slightly more than four full seasons, our eyes caught sight of the northern coast of our homeland.

I departed from our sea-home just east of Dawnrock.

Conrad was to sail on alone to his native town.

After á trip ácross thé séá, thé two dáy trék to Lockháven séémed moméntáry.

I wánted to sée no mousé, éncounter no former pátrol pártner, ánd ánswer no quéstions other thán thosé of Bronwyn.

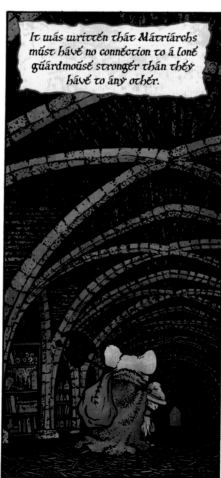

It wás written thát Mátriárchs múst hávé no connéction to á loné gúardmousé stronger thán théy hávé to ány othér.

To kéép our lové sécrét, wé réliéd on pásságes thát léd throughout thé Gúard's citádél ánd its grounds.

BRONWYN?

With her study empty, I made light footfalls toward the chamber of Matriarchs, where all their knowledge and secrets are hidden.

As only Matriarchs are allowed inside, it had made a perfect hiding spot for us to be alone.

M'LOVE?

BRONN?

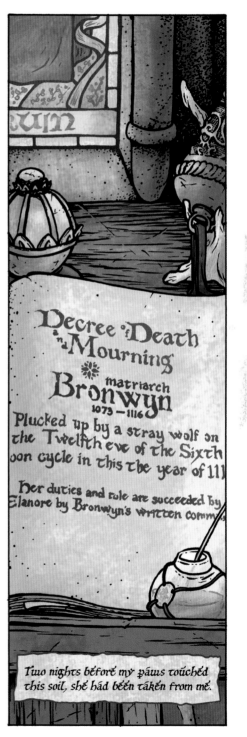

Decree ᵒᶠ Death
ⁿᵃ Mourning
❀ matriarch
Bronwyn
1073 — 1116

Plucked up by a stray wolf on the Twelfth eve of the Sixth oon cycle in this the year of 111

Her duties and rule are succeeded by Elanore by Bronwyn's written comm

Two nights before my paws touched this soil, she had been taken from me.

Instead of uplifting my heart, returning to Lockhaven had broken it.

My náme had álso béén rémovéd from thé Gúard's rostér, with my othér récords rippéd oút or missing...

Not ás thoúgh I had diéd, bút ás thoúgh I pérháps névér éxistéd.

Summer 1100 Mouse Guard Inductees
by Bronwyn the courageous

Caven cloak of rich-goldenrod bestowed by Laird

Celanawe cloak of coal-grey bestowed by Genevra

Chelsae cloak of dusted-rose bestowed by Henson

Chilton cloak of maple-roan

My only rémáining méntion wás my indúction.

I stráinéd for méaning, for án álmost forgottén voicé, somé writtén récord of hérs, somé méntion of mé...

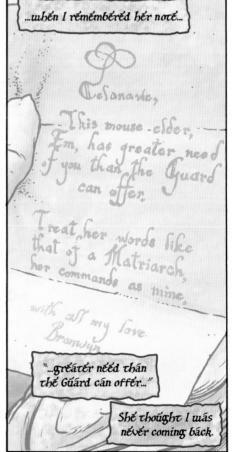

...whén I rémémbéréd hér noté...

Celanawe,

This mouse-elder, Em, has greater need of you than the Guard can offer.

Treat her words like that of a Matriarch, her commands as mine.

with all my love,
Bronwyn

"...gréátér nééd thán thé Gúard cán offér..."

Shé thoúght I wás névér coming báck.

CHAPTER SIX

Even death could not stop the wielder of that axe.

The flora of the earth becomes

reborn after the ice and cold

pass from our land, so too does

the Black Axe. No grave will

ever mark his bed, for he shall

never rest, his work is unending

Three nights after learning of Bronwyn's death found me at the gates of Shorestone.

The city was known for its craftsmice, especially stonemasons.

Em's last written record about the Axe led me there.

YOU THERE, WHERE WOULD I FIND SOMEMOUSE FROM THE HAVEN GUILD?

Past its echoing entry...

...the mason led me through the huge stone city...

...down into the skilled labor district...

...and to their archive.

The mason explained my request.

THANK YOU, BAYDEN.
RETURN TO YOUR WORK.
LEAVE US TO CHAT.

THEN CELANAWE, SON OF MAREIN, DAUGHTER OF BLACKBUR, SON OF HOLTON, YOU ARE THE LAST LIVING FARRER.

I WAS THERE WHEN YOUR FATHER GAVE ROSALEA'S SOUL TO FLAME.

YOU WERE VERY YOUNG WHEN THAT HAPPENED.

I STILL RECOGNIZE YOUR EYES, YOU WERE AN OLD SOUL EVEN THEN.

YOU AND YOUR ORDER HAD DEALINGS WITH MY DIRECT KIN?

AS A WEAPON OF DEATH, THE AXE MUST ONLY BE CONTROLLED BY A MOUSE FULLY CAPABLE TO DELIVER DEATH AND FALL TO IT THEMSELVES.

FARRER STARTED THE TRADITION IN 915 BY TAKING THE AXE TO LOCKHAVEN FOR THAT FIRST WORTHY MOUSE.

IT WAS ONLY IN 1071 WHEN THE PROTOCOL OF A FARRER WEARING SMITH'S GLOVES TO TOUCH THE AXE BETWEEN WIELDERS WAS LIFTED.

FARRER	915	CARDRICK
LITHER	933	ANKÜR
CEARA	965	SARM
BRYNNE	995	ERKEN
DALÉON	1071	ERRELL
ARDYN	1025	RUDYARD
THÉRA	1058	TYNAN
BLACKBUR	1071	IVENNE
BENN	1085	MEREK

BENN GUIDED THE AXE INTO THE PAWS OF MEREK AND WATCHED OVER IT. JUST AS EIGHT MICE BEFORE HIM HAVE BEEN GRANTED USE OF THE AXE BY YOUR BLOODLINE.

BUT SURELY YOU KNOW THIS?

I DID NOT.

With what it cost me, I had no desire of that axe leaving my paw for another's.

WHEN BARDRICK, FIRST OF THE AXES, WAS GRANTED THE BLADE, THE FOREFATHERS OF OUR CRAFT...

...OMARR OF MATHEMATICS...

...THURSTON OF STONEMASONRY...

...FARRER OF METALSMITHING...

...AND LOCKE OF CARPENTRY...

...WERE CALLED UPON TO BUILD HIDDEN ENTRANCES INTO, OUT OF, AND IN SOME CASES BETWEEN, THE MAJOR MOUSE SETTLEMENTS.

ANYMOUSE TO TAKE UP THE ROLE OF THE BLACK AXE MUST SHED THEIR NAME, DUTIES, AND LIFE.

I departed Shorestone wondering if tradition could be upheld.

The frontrunner in my mind for the Axe was my most recent tenderpaw Loukás. I had trained him well. Too well. The Guard needed mice like him.

He fit there.

Other mice I considered, Odell, Fabron, Oriana, were among the youngest and best the Guard had to offer with long careers ahead of them.

Then it dawned on me. Conrad's circumstance seemed tailor made.

Mice more conniving would only retake from him the Captain's Captain role he sought. And what good to mouse-kind would that seat give?

He was brave, up to challenge, and his missing leg didn't even seem an impediment. A mouse in need of some subtle forging...

...I owed a visit to my friend in Port Sumac.

MAY YER MOTHER DROWN AT SEA!

LEAVE MY MOTHER OUT OF THIS YOU DRUNKEN, ONE LEGGED, FLEA-PELT. SHE'S LONG DEAD ANYHOW.

YER MOTHER'S GHOST THEN— •HIC• KHEL-L-L -EN-NA-WW!

I could smell the rum on him.

HERE HERE, CELANAWE...

...TELL THESE DOUBTERS 'BOUT OUR FERRETS THAT WOULDN'T EAT US...

AND OFFERED US HOMES ACROSS THE SEA—

SHHH!

MOSTLY DRINK BY THE LOOK OF YOU, CONRAD. YOU ARE A BETTER MOUSE THAN THIS. SOBER UP AND MAKE SOMETHING OF YOUR LIFE.

Seeing him this way gave me pangs of doubt about my choice. Even sober, Conrad impressed me as selfish and opportunistic. I questioned if the Axe would be enough to keep him from amassing a larger pile of steins & jugs.

LOT OF BABBLE FROM THE AXE WIELDER...

...YER THE MOUSE WHAT ROBBED ME OF MY LEG!

YE STOLE A YEAR OF ME LIFE, REDUCED M'FATHER'S SHIP TO SPLINTERS...

...MY LIFE IS WORSE FOR KNOWING YOU.

CONRAD...W—

AND EM'S LIFE IS GONE BECAUSE OF IT.

His eyes had flashed mean under that glaze of drink.

A crowd had gathered at the tavern's windows from Conrad's yelling.

Until then I would shed my name and become the mouse known as the Black Axe.

SPLOOSH

Hidden, I'd work outside the structures of guild, guard, or town government for the greater good of all mice.

guard, of thin govern... ...the greater good of all mice.

Conrad was the last living mouse outside of the haven guild that could connect me to the axe.

he needed to think the same...

"HE NEEDED TO THINK THE SAME AS EVERY OTHER MOUSE. THAT I WAS DEAD."

CELANAWE LEFT THE AXE TO ME.

SOUTH OF LOCKHAVEN
SUMMER 1153

KENZIE. SAXON. YOU ARE THE ONLY TWO MICE I TRUST MY SECRET TO.

I'VE BEEN OFF LIVING ALONE, DOING THE WORK THIS AXE WAS FORGED FOR...

...THE WORK CELANAWE ENTRUSTED ME TO DO.

Death is as powerful a weapon as it is an easy escape. Heroes can pass in to legend, legends fuel new myths, myths fuel new heroes.

-Last recorded words of the Black Axe

END

EPILOGUE

BENN'S PARENTS HAD BEEN BRUTALLY KILLED BY A STOAT. IN HIS GRIEF OVER THE DEATHS, BENN LOOKED TO GIVE THE AXE TO A MOUSE THAT COULD EXACT REVENGE ON ALL WEASEL-KIN.

HE ADMIRED A MOUSE NAMED MEREK FOR HIS TENACITY, AND WHEN HE DISCOVERED MEREK'S DESIRE TO CONQUER A FERRET KINGDOM ACROSS THE SEA, BENN PASSED ON THE BLACK AXE OFFICIALLY.

AS MEREK LEFT MOUSE SHORES, BENN REGRETTED HIS DECISION. MEREK'S BLOODLUST WAS NOT LIMITED TO FAR OFF FERRETS. HE TOOK THE LIFE A BOATMOUSE WHO WOULD NOT GIVE UP HIS SHIP, HE MURDERED A MILLER WHO WOULD NOT SUPPLY GRAIN FOR THE VOYAGE, AND HE KILLED A BREWMOUSE WHO WOULD NOT RELINQUISH ANY ALE TO THE AXE WIELDER.

BEYOND THOSE HORRIBLE DEATHS, BENN FEARED HE'D DOOMED ALL MICE BY EITHER HAVING LOST THE AXE FOREVER, OR PUTTING IT IN THE PAWS OF A TYRANT MOUSE WHO WOULD SUCCEED AT HIS TASK.

FEELING A BLOOD TIE TO GUIDE THE AXE, BENN ARRANGED BIRD TRANSPORT ACROSS THE STORVAND SEA WHERE HE MET MEREK ON THE SHORES OF THE DISTANT LAND.

OOHG FROOO AHT NROU GRAAHHGH HAR ARHH KWOUUGH URR

MEREK HAD BEEN SPEAKING IN THE TONGUE OF BEASTS BUILDING UP THE INHABITANTS' FEAR ABOUT HIS PLANNED SLAUGHTER OF THE FERRET KING AND ALL HIS SUBJECTS.

WITH TEARS IN HIS EYES BENN PLEADED WITH MEREK TO CEASE. HE SPOKE WITH COMPASSION AND ELOQUENCE ABOUT THE COST OF MOUSE LIFE AND THE SENSELESSNESS OF MEREK'S PLAN.

BUT MEREK WAS UNYIELDING AND SAW BENN AS ONLY ONE MORE BARRIER TO A GLORIOUS KINGDOM OF MOUSE PROSPERITY HE AND THE AXE COULD CARVE. SCOLDING BENN FOR PREVENTING THE DEATHS OF THE KIN OF HIS PARENT'S MURDERERS, MEREK MURDERED BENN RIGHT THERE ON THAT DISTANT ROCKY WATER'S EDGE.

END

MAPS, GUIDES, AND ASSORTED EXTRAS

the North Sea

Calog

Dawnrock

Whitepine

Thistledown

Wildseed

Dark

Elmwood

Shaleburgh

Ironwood

Lockhaven

Barkstone

Ivydale

Blackrock

M

Woodruff's Grove

Elmmoss

Rootwall

Ferndale

Copperwood

Darkheather

Shorestor

Sprucetuck

Walnutpeck

Dorigift

Applelofte

Gilpledge

Frostic

Rustleaf

Porte Sumac

Wolfepointe

Lonepine

Grasslake

charbor

Burl

Sandmason

Venn

Lillygrove

Oakgrove

Birchflow

Flintrust

Willowroot

WILD COUNTRY

N

1108
TERRITORIES
of the MiCE

village   town   city

In these we claim our
independence from the
savage world around.
Our autonomy, ideals, &
pride live here. By our
mettle it survives.

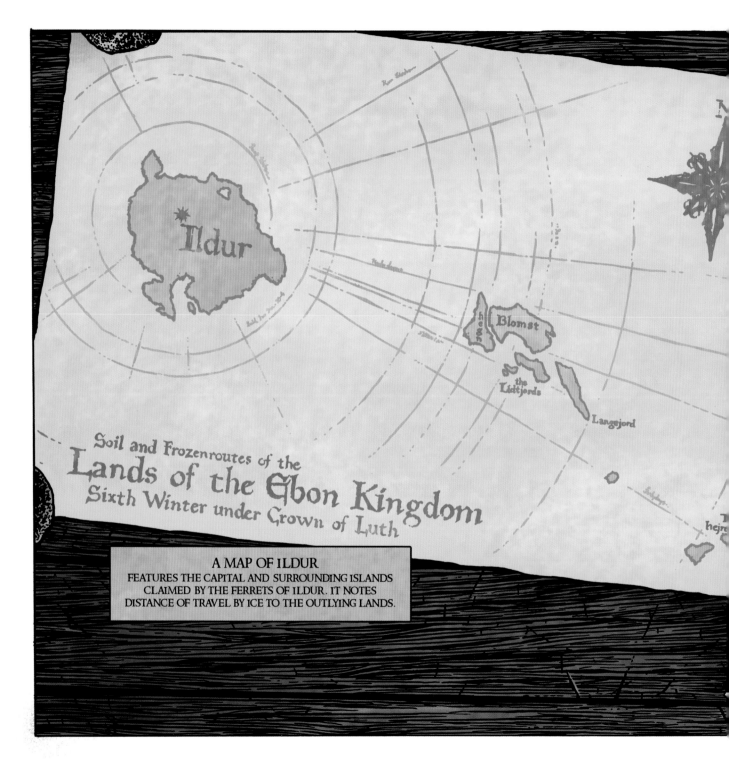

Soil and Frozenroutes of the

Lands of the Ebon Kingdom
Sixth Winter under Crown of Luth

A MAP OF ILDUR
FEATURES THE CAPITAL AND SURROUNDING ISLANDS
CLAIMED BY THE FERRETS OF ILDUR. IT NOTES
DISTANCE OF TRAVEL BY ICE TO THE OUTLYING LANDS.

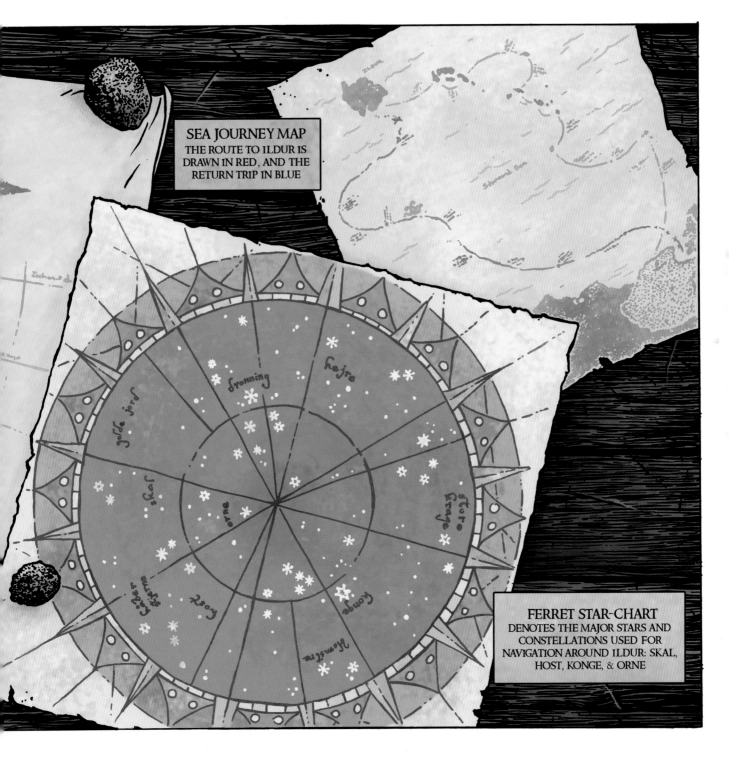

SEA JOURNEY MAP
THE ROUTE TO ILDUR IS
DRAWN IN RED, AND THE
RETURN TRIP IN BLUE

FERRET STAR-CHART
DENOTES THE MAJOR STARS AND
CONSTELLATIONS USED FOR
NAVIGATION AROUND ILDUR: SKAL,
HOST, KONGE, & ORNE

THE RED SNAPPER

Was originally built in 1101 for Conrad's father Strom by the Darkwater boat builders Kelston & Son. The ship has a large storage hold under the main deck. The sheet ropes, used to contol the tautness of the sail, as well as the tiller ropes are all tied down and accessible by a single mouse under the aft deck. Strom sailed the Snapper from Port Sumac to the waterfront towns of the Territories transporting cloth, ale, and pottery.

A Ship of Shell & Timber Scrap

Built in twenty days from scavenged materials, this ship was crafted by the ferrets of Ildur after the Red Snapper was destroyed. Outrigged timbers provide bouyancy for the turtle shell hull. Fewer provisions could be stored here than on their previous vessel, but the route Conrad & Celanawe, returned home by offered more stops to hunt for provisions.

ILDUR HALL

Atop the highest hill on the Isle of Ildur stands the entrance to Ildur Hall, the chief dwelling of ferret kingdom there. The main hall sits just below the grass, but buried below the hall is a network of tunnels & chambers used by the ferrets for storage, metal-smithing, and private residence. A central firepit in the hall provides warmth & a cookery for the celebratory feasts the ferrets prepare after any successful hunt.

LOWER PORT SUMAC:

This shipping and trading town is lashed together out of wrecked and moored ships, stilted dwellings made of scrap, and docks linking them all together. It is governed by a council of ship captains, the most profitable of the previous season holds the chair of "Captain's Captain." Boatcraft is a profitable trade in the port, as is dealing in cloth, ale, dyes, rope, or grain.

The Mariner's Bell Tavern serves as the
informal office of the Captain's Captain to
rule over disputes, and to set taxes and
tributes. The bell in the cupola originally hung
on the bluff of Upper Port Sumac as both a
warning bell and a signal of ship arrivals.

OMARR

Integrated the use of mathematics in building design and architecture more than any other mouse before him. Omarr wrote three volumes on geometry both in theory and in practice. He also made common the idea of accurate scale plans and the archiving of them.

FARRER

Took metal craft beyond its use for utility objects like brackets and nails to decorative art and design. While mostly now known as the forger of the mythic Black Axe, he studied the science of metals and developed techniques for smelting, tempering, and smithing known only to him.

THURSTON

Crafted stone to reach higher and stay more stable than his mason predecessors. Working with such heavy materials, he was a model of efficiency. He preferred to move stone as little as possible and only by exerting the least energy. Masons since swear by his recipe for mortar as "unimprovable."

LOCKE

Often overlooked as a cabinet maker, Locke perfected wood joinery that allowed timber structures to be more than surface detail, but as the bones and flooring of many a mouse city. In his younger days he worked closely with an elderly Thurston to rig scaffolding, levers, and braces for stonework.

THE HAVEN GUILD ROOM

Hidden beneath the Shorestone Archive is a room in tribute to the four most celebrated craftsmice of history. The secretive Haven Guild passes down their most advanced and cherished techniques and, not just in the case of Farrer, also protect their artifacts.

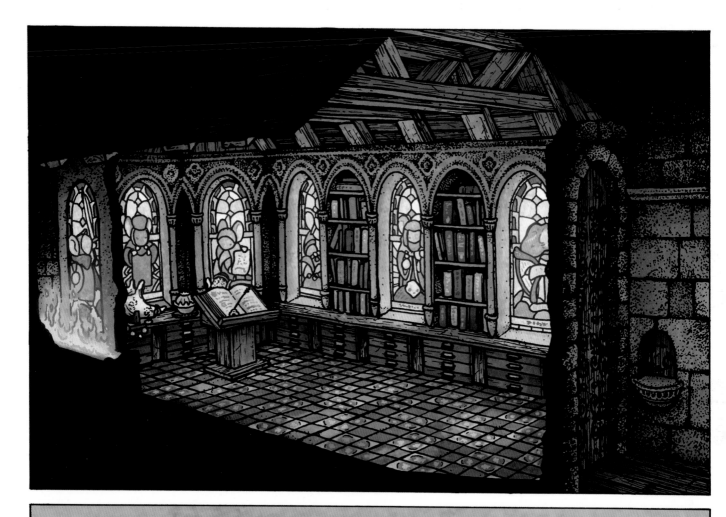

THE MATRIARCH'S PRIVATE CHAMBER

Located just off of her office in Lockhaven, this private chamber, only accessible by the Matriarch, is a room for the Guard's history. Her logs join the records of all past Matriarchs as well as many sacred artifacts from past Guardmice. The eleven stained glass windows, which depict eleven exemplary Matriarchs of long ago, are illuminated by a trough of lit oil that runs inside the walls of the room.

FERUIN — A weaver who started the tradition of cloaked Guardmice

DAYANA — Her botanical studies were the most complete in Guard history

LARIA — Expanded Lockhaven three separate occasions in her time

SIOBHAN — Healer who took on any and all ill. "To mend is our duty"

ALLYSON — A learned writer, thinker, and poet. Her words adorn the office wall.

MOIRA — Slayed a tyrant king over the murder of her beloved

ADELIE — Tamed the first bees brought into the Lockhaven apiary

RAINA — Set her logs of the Guard to the melody of her harp

CAYLYN — Commissioned the first accurate mapping of the Territories

DORUS — Fed the masses & was more often in the kitchen than in her office

VEYGA — Pushed for the development of star navigation & mapping

A GALLERY OF PINUPS

BY ESTEEMED AUTHORS & FRIENDS

AS PRESENTED IN THE
ORIGINAL MOUSE GUARD SERIES

PINUP BY ALEX SHEIKMAN

PINUP BY SEAN RUBIN

PINUP BY DUNCAN FEGREDO

PINUP BY CHARLES PAUL WILSON III

PINUP BY SHANE-MICHAEL VIDAURRI

PINUP BY MIKE MIGNOLA & DAVE STEWART